Published 1986 by
Hamlyn Publishing,
A division of The Hamlyn Publishing Group Ltd,
Bridge House, London Road, Twickenham, Middlesex, England

© 1984 ICA-förlaget AB,
John Pohlman, Maja Elmér
and SVT Multimedia

ISBN 0 600 31116 3
Printed in Italy

Conceived and planned in
co-operation with Maja
Elmér

Illustrations: Lars Klinting
Additional Illustrations: Vincent Driver, Robin Lawrie
Photographs: BBC Enterprises p58; Crown copyright material is
    reproduced with the permission of the Controller of Her Majesty's Stationary
    Office pp55, 59; Ola Inghe p37 bottom; Bertil Karlen p22;
    Frank Lane Picture Library pp44–5; Christer Morales; NASA, Washington
    DC p30; NOAA p46
Symbols on p60 reproduced with permission of BBC
Design: Anders Rahm

All About The Weather

JOHN POHLMAN

Introduced by Ian McCaskill

HAMLYN

Contents

Introduction

I am a happy man. Among my hobbies are geology (the earth beneath) and meteorology (the sky above). As a result I can't make a journey, or even step out of the door without being knocked over by the wonder of it all. The rocks, it is true, don't do a lot – they just lie there looking interesting. But the sky is always busy and infinitely varied. A very little knowledge unlocks her secrets. This book provides the key.

Read it and you will understand why I find the weather so endlessly fascinating. And you will learn some actual numbers too (shock, horror!). The delightful illustrations will help you reach a real understanding of the scale of the elements which produce weather, from the planets to the tiny droplets in a cloud.

This is an excellent and engaging introduction to the weather. Perhaps there should be a publisher's warning on the back: THIS BOOK MAY UNSERIOUSLY AFFECT YOUR APPRECIATION OF THE TOP HALF OF YOUR WORLD.

Ian McCaskill

Sun

Earth

The Sun, The Earth and Climate

The Sun is an enormous burning ball of gas. The temperature on the surface is 5,000 to 6,000°C (9,000 to 11,000°F). The heat from the Sun streams out into space.

The nine large planets which circle the Sun are shown below. The planet nearest the Sun is called Mercury. Further away in order are Venus, Earth, Mars, Jupiter, Saturn, Uranus, Neptune and Pluto, which is the furthest from the Sun.

The Earth is just the right distance from the Sun for it to be neither too hot nor too cold for life to exist. It is like being near a bonfire. If you are too near you will be too hot and if you are too far away from the fire you will not feel its warmth. It is too hot for there to be life on the planets nearest the Sun, where temperatures can reach 460°C (865°F). The planets which are further from the Sun are too cold, with temperatures which can be less than −200°C (−330°F).

THE SUN AND THE EARTH

The distance from the Earth to the Sun is about 150 million kilometres (93 million miles). That is like putting nearly 12,000 globes the size of the Earth in a row.

If we pretended that the Sun was the size of a big beach ball, then the Earth would be a little pea more than 100 metres (110 yards) away. The Sun is more than one million times as big as the Earth.

120 metres (130 yards)

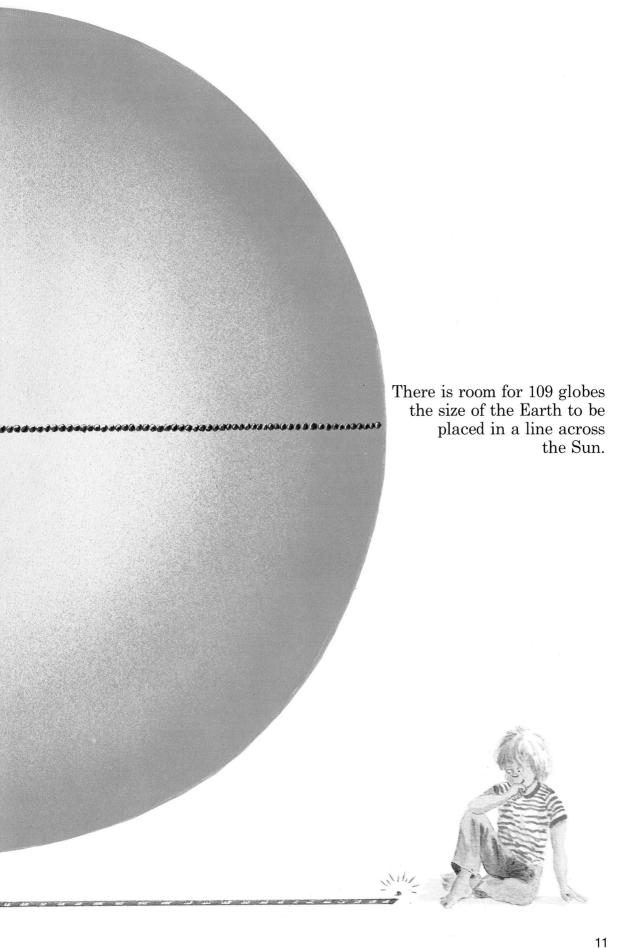

There is room for 109 globes
the size of the Earth to be
placed in a line across
the Sun.

THE SEASONS

The North Pole is tilted towards the Sun. This is summer in the Northern Hemisphere.

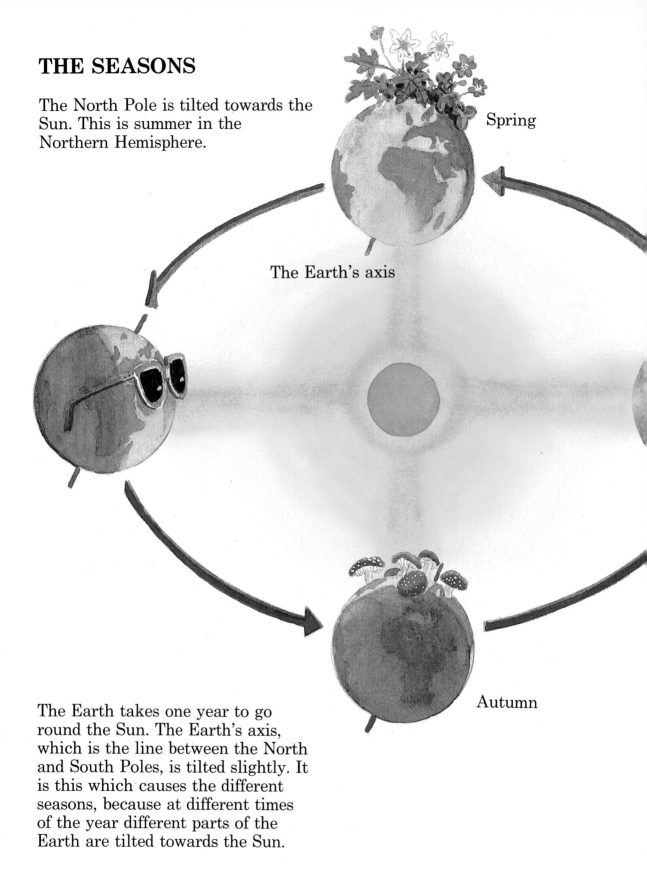

Spring

The Earth's axis

Autumn

The Earth takes one year to go round the Sun. The Earth's axis, which is the line between the North and South Poles, is tilted slightly. It is this which causes the different seasons, because at different times of the year different parts of the Earth are tilted towards the Sun.

The North Pole is tilted away from the Sun. This is winter in the Northern Hemisphere.

DAY AND NIGHT

The Sun only lights one side of the Earth at a time. The side in darkness experiences night and the lit side has daytime. Because the Earth is also revolving on its own axis, once every 24 hours, days and nights follow each other.

When it is day in Europe and Africa it is night in Hawaii and Australia. At the same time it is evening in Asia and morning in America.

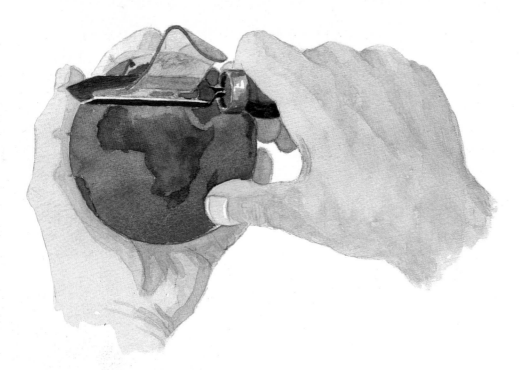

Exosphere

_____

THE ATMOSPHERE

There is a layer of air around the
Earth. This is called the
atmosphere. Without this layer of
air we would not be able to live and
breathe. It is very thin, rather like
the peel on an apple (above).

    The lowest part of the atmosphere
is called the troposphere (right) and
goes up for a height of 10 to 15
kilometres (6 to 10 miles).
Everything which we call weather
takes place in the troposphere –
clouds, rain and snow, wind and
thunderstorms.

    Higher up is the stratosphere and
even further up is the ionosphere
and the exosphere.

    The air becomes thinner and
thinner as you go higher up and in
the exosphere there is hardly any
air at all.

    There is no air on the Moon.
Since there is no air, there cannot
be any weather – no clouds, never
any rain or snow and no wind.

Ionosphere

_____

Stratosphere

_____

Troposphere

_____

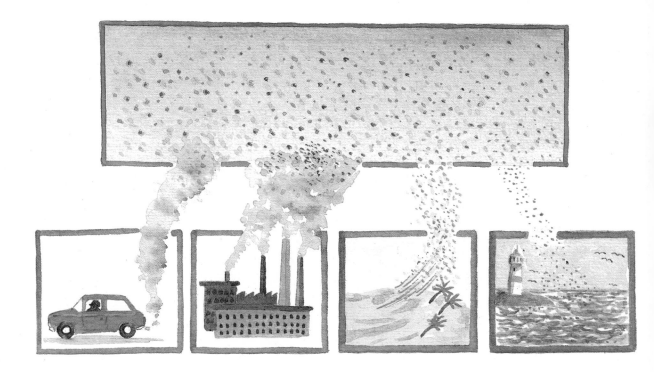

PARTICLES IN THE AIR

The air around the Earth is made up of a number of different gases which are invisible. It is mainly nitrogen and oxygen.

There are also many particles in the air. These include dirt and smoke from car exhausts and chimneys, tiny grains of sand blown up by storms and tiny particles of salt from the sea, as the illustration above shows.

RAYS FROM THE SUN AND WARMTH FROM THE EARTH

The rays of light from the Sun move through space very quickly. Their speed is approximately 300,000 kilometres per second (186,000 miles per second). It only takes about eight minutes for a light ray to travel from the Sun to the Earth.

When rays from the Sun reach the Earth, they first meet the air surrounding the Earth. Lower down nearer the Earth the rays meet clouds and tiny particles in the atmosphere. Part of a ray is reflected back into space or absorbed by the clouds and the particles. But almost half of the ray gets through and warms the surface of the Earth. This is illustrated above.

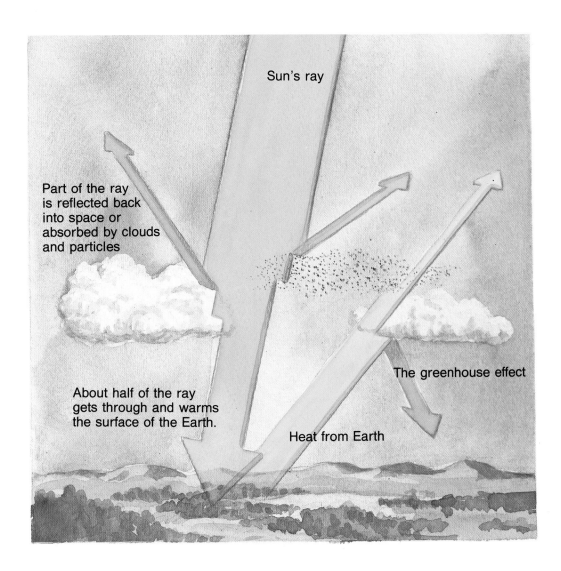

Sun's ray

Part of the ray is reflected back into space or absorbed by clouds and particles

About half of the ray gets through and warms the surface of the Earth.

The greenhouse effect

Heat from Earth

The surface of the Earth and the atmosphere also loose heat, radiating it back out into space. If this did not happen the Earth would just get hotter and hotter. The heat from the Earth meets the clouds and the particles in the atmosphere. Just as with the Sun's rays, some of the heat from the Earth is reflected and some is absorbed by the clouds and the particles. But unlike the Sun's rays, almost half of which get through the atmosphere and reach the Earth, most of the heat from the Earth is used up heating the air around it. This is called the greenhouse effect, since the atmosphere acts like the glass in a greenhouse.

So it is not the Sun's rays which heat up the air, but warmth from the Earth. It is a bit like a hot-plate on a cooker. That is why it gets colder as you go higher up in the air and further away from the Earth.

MEASURING THE TEMPERATURE

When people want to measure how hot or cold it is, they need to know the temperature of the air. The air is warmed up by the Earth, not by the Sun.

A thermometer in the Sun measures both the warmth coming from the surface of the Earth (the air temperature) and the warmth from the Sun's rays which are shining upon the thermometer. To measure the temperature of the air, the thermometer must therefore be in the shade (as above).

When the Sun's rays meet particles high up in the air, the sunlight is split up into different colours and scattered in all directions. The blue colour is scattered most and that is why the sky looks blue.

When the Sun's rays meet soot and dust particles lower down in the atmosphere the colours are absorbed. The blue colour is affected the most and the red colour the least. When the Sun is low down on the horizon, for example at sunset, the rays have to go further through the atmosphere than when the Sun is high in the sky. Therefore the blue colour and the other colours gradually vanish and finally only the red is left, producing a beautiful red sunset.

So it is the air and the atmosphere which make the sky coloured. If there were no atmosphere the sky would be completely black and the Sun would look like a white ball. This is what it looks like on the Moon.

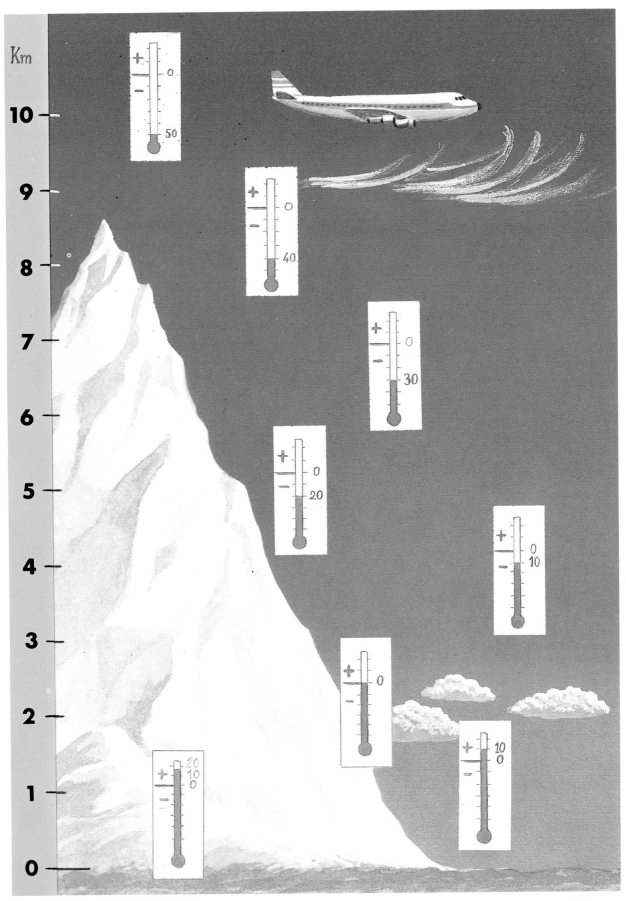

The temperature normally drops as height increases. It becomes 5 to 10°C (9 to 18°F) colder for every kilometre (8 to 16°C (14 to 28°F) for every mile) higher you go.

THE EARTH'S CLIMATE

The further the Sun's rays have to go through the atmosphere, the more particles and clouds they meet. This means that less of the ray gets through to the Earth's surface. For this reason it is warmer when the Sun is high in the sky at midday than during the morning or evening when the Sun is nearer the horizon.

That is also why it is warmer at the Equator than at the Poles.

The different angles at which the Sun's rays reach the Earth means that some places on the Earth are hotter or colder than others. It also rains (or snows) more in some places than others. Thus different places on the Earth have different climates. The average weather over many years is called the climate.

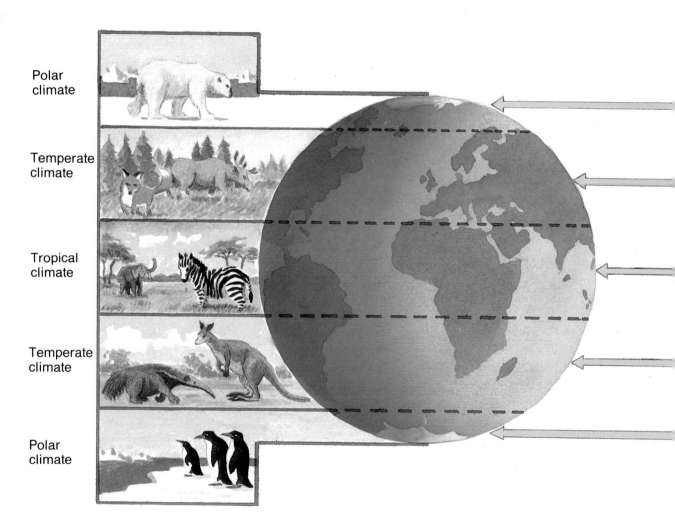

Polar climate

Temperate climate

Tropical climate

Temperate climate

Polar climate

At the Poles the Sun's rays have the longest distance to travel through the atmosphere. The rays are also spread over a greater surface area, since the Earth is round.

The Sun's rays have the shortest distance to travel through the atmosphere at the Equator. Here the rays meet the surface of the Earth almost vertically.

Polar climate

At the Poles it is cold all the year round. The ground is frozen and covered with snow or ice.

Temperate climate

Temperate regions have climates which are changeable with different seasons. Precipitation (rain or snow) occurs all year round.

There are three types of temperate climate: continental climate (cold winters and hot summers), coastal climate (mild winters and cool summers) and mediterranean climate (mild unsettled winters and hot dry summers).

Tropical climate

The tropics are hot all the year round. There are different types of tropical climate, depending upon the rainfall. They include desert climate (little or no rain), steppe and savanna climate (rain at certain times of the year, drought at other times) and rainforest climate (humid with rain all the year round).

The Air and The Wind

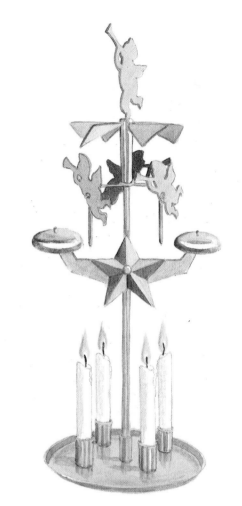

The air around the Earth is almost never still. It is moving nearly all the time, both across the surface of the Earth and up and down. Air which moves is called wind.

Air rises when it is warm. In the illustration on the right the candle flames heat the air nearest to them. The warm air rises and hits the rotor blades below the top angel. This causes the blades to rotate and makes the angels move round. As they go round, the angels hit the bells with their sticks.

A hot-air balloon rises because the air inside the balloon is heated up (below).

RISING AIR

In Nature it is the surface of the Earth (which is heated by the Sun) that heats up the air nearest the ground. The warm air rises producing a rising wind (above). This rising current of air is called a thermal and is used by glider pilots and birds. Using thermals, a glider can fly upwards without an engine and birds can stay in the air with their wings outstretched but motionless.

The reason that air rises when it is warm is that it expands, becomes lighter than the surrounding air and rises just like a cork in water. When it cools the air sinks down again.

AIR PRESSURE

You cannot see air but you can still measure it. This is done with an instrument called a barometer,

which is a kind of weighing machine. The barometer measures how much all the air above the instrument weighs. This measurement is called the air pressure since the weight of the air exerts a downwards pressure.

Air pressure drops as you go up, since the higher you go, the less air there is above you. The blue bars in the illustration above represent the amount of air in the atmosphere bearing down on people at different heights. Air pressure also drops when the air is warmed up, since that makes the air lighter and it weighs less. An area of warm air where the air pressure is lower than in the surrounding area is called a low-pressure area. An area of cool air with higher pressure than the surrounding area is called a high-pressure area.

When there is high pressure the weather is often sunny and fine.

When there is low pressure it is often cloudy with rain or snow.

SEA BREEZES

When warm air rises, it is replaced by air flowing from surrounding areas where the air pressure is higher. This is nature's way of correcting an imbalance. Just as water runs from a place where there is a lot of water to a place where there is less, so air moves from areas of high pressure (a lot of air) to areas of low pressure (less air).

The movement of the air (the wind) depends upon the air being heated differently in different places and creating areas of low pressure. A good example is a sea breeze.

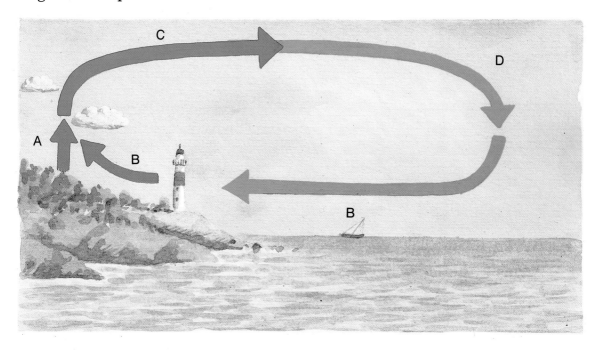

Sunny summer days warm up the land more rapidly than the water. The land in turn warms up the air nearest to it which rises (A in the illustration above). The air pressure is then lower over the land than over the water and air moves in from the sea. The land warms up the air from the sea and it too rises (B).

When the air from the land (A) has risen, it cools down a little and flows out over the sea (C). Here it is cooled downn ven more, becomes heavier and begins to sink (D). In this way the air circulates between the sea and the land.

MONSOON WINDS

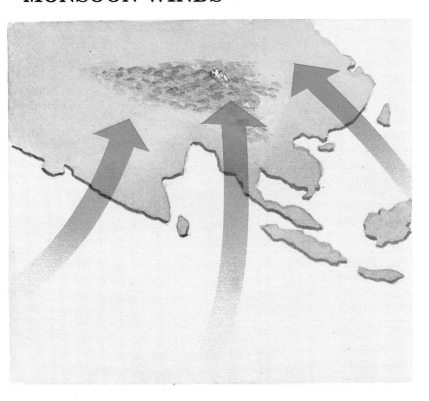

Summer

Large-scale sea breezes are called monsoons. In the summer the continents warm up more rapidly than the oceans. A large low-pressure area forms over the land and the cooler sea air streams in. The sea air is moist and often brings rain.

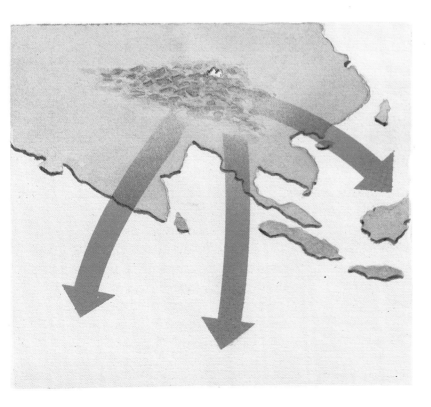

Winter

Just as the land heats up more rapidly than the water, so it cools down more rapidly. During the winter conditions are therefore reversed. The colder, heavier air forms a high-pressure area over the land and air moves from the continents out over the oceans.

The arrows show
how the trade
winds blow

high pressure

low pressure

high pressure

low pressure

high pressure

low pressure

high pressure

LOW PRESSURE AND HIGH PRESSURE

The variations in the heating of the Earth (see page 20) result in various high-pressure and low-pressure belts around the Earth.

The area around the equator receives the most rays from the Sun. The air in the equatorial region is heated up, becomes lighter and rises. This results in a belt of low pressure around the equator. When the rising air at the equator has risen into the atmosphere, it cools and flows outwards to the north and south.

There it cools even more (as in a sea breeze) and sinks down to form a high-pressure belt on each side of the equatorial region.

The movement of the air from the high-pressure belts to the low-

pressure belt on the equator produces what we call the trade winds. The high-pressure belts have little cloud and not much rain.

The rays from the Sun which fall on the Polar regions are the weakest that reach the Earth. There the air is cold and heavy and forms a high-pressure area around the North and South Poles.

Between these high-pressure belts at the Poles and the high-pressure belts above and below the equator there are belts which are mostly occupied by areas of low pressure. The low-pressure areas in these belts usually move from west to east. Sometimes an area of low pressure will stop and remain still for a while. Between the low-pressure areas there are high-pressure areas or ridges which, like the low-pressure areas, move eastwards or remain still. Thus the weather in this belt is changeable.

If the Earth did not move, air would move straight from the high-pressure areas to the low-pressure areas. But because the Earth is turning on its axis the air is moved sideways as well. This makes the air spiral outwards from the high-pressure areas and inwards to the low-pressure areas. Thus the air circulates around high- and low-pressure areas.

In the Northern Hemisphere air moves clockwise around a high-pressure area and anti-clockwise around a low-pressure area. In the Southern Hemisphere it is the other way round – air moves anti-clockwise around high-pressure and clockwise around low-pressure.

If you stand with the wind blowing on your back (as above), high pressure will be on your right and low pressure on your left. In the Southern Hemisphere the high pressure will be on your left. The rising air of the low-pressure area produces clouds and perhaps rain, while the sinking air of the high-pressure area often gives clear weather.

Calm. 0 km/h (0 mph). No movement from leaves and twigs. Smoke rises vertically. Flags and pennants hang straight down. The sea is as smooth as glass.

Light breeze. 6–12 km/h (4–7 mph). Leaves begin to move. Smoke drifts in the direction of the wind. Pennants lift a little. Ripples and small waves on the sea.

Moderate breeze. 21–29 km/h (13–18 mph). Twigs and small branches move. Dust and powdered snow are picked up by the wind. Pennants fly fully extended. Waves on the sea begin to break.

Fresh breeze. 30–39 km/h (19–24 mph). Small trees begin to sway. Dust and powdered snow is whirled up into the air. Telephone wires hum. At sea there are larger, longer waves with a lot of white foam.

WIND SPEED

Wind is air which moves. Air moves to reduce differences between areas with different amounts of air.

Air moves in a spiral from high-pressure areas (with more air) to low-pressure areas (with less air).

The greater the difference between the high pressure and the low pressure, the greater the quantity of a

This view of a hurricane from space shows the way in which its winds blow in a spiral.

which moves and the greater the speed at which it moves – in other words, the windier it is. Wind is usually measured by measuring how far the air moves in a certain time. This is called the wind speed. A fresh breeze of 34 km/h (21 mph) has the same speed as a car travelling at 34 km/h (21 mph).

Strong breeze. Gale. 40–74 km/h (25–46 mph). Whole trees sway and bend. Twigs break off. It is difficult to walk outside. Some damage maybe done to houses – roof tiles are blown off. Large breakers form at sea and spray is whirled into the air.

Storm. 89–102 km/h (55–63 mph). Trees are uprooted. Widespread damage is done to houses and vegetation. It is dangerous to be outside. Very high waves form at sea with long breakers. The surface of the sea is covered with foam.

Hurricane. More than 117 km/h (73 mph). Tremendous amounts of damage are done to buildings and Nature. It is extremely dangerous to be outside. Enormous waves develop at sea.

THE COOLING EFFECT OF THE WIND

In summer the wind is refreshing on hot days. In winter it feels even colder when the wind is blowing. This is because the wind blows away a warm layer of air which is next to the skin. When it is extremely cold and very windy it is possible to get frostbite, a dangerous condition in which parts of the body freeze and circulation stops.

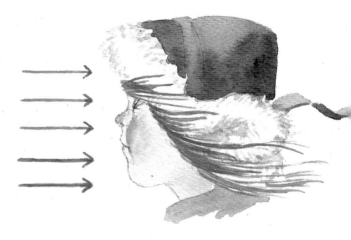

Next to the skin there is a thin layer of air which is warmed by the heat from the body.

The warm-air layer which protects the skin is blown away by the wind and the cold air can reach the skin.

Temperature when calm	Temperature under same conditions but with a wind	
	Wind speed 18 km/h (12 mph)	Wind speed 36 km/h (24 mph)
0°C (32°F)	−10°C (14°F)	−15°C (5°F)
−10°C (14°F)	−20°C (−4°F)	−30°C (−22°F)
−25°C (−13°F)	−40°C (−40°F)	−50°C (−58°F)

The chill factor

This table shows how much colder it feels when there is a wind compared with when it is calm.

FORMATION OF FRONTS

Cold air and warm air do not like mixing together (it is like trying to mix oil and water). When they meet, the heavier cold air goes under the warm air which is forced upwards. The line where cold air and warm air meet is called a front.

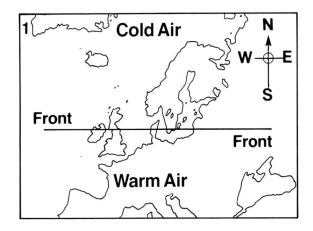

This is how it looks to start with. The cold air and the warm air are separate and a front divides them.

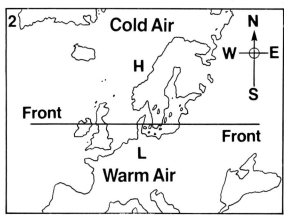

The cold air is heavier than the warm and its air pressure is higher. A high-pressure area forms in the cold air and a low-pressure area in the warm air.

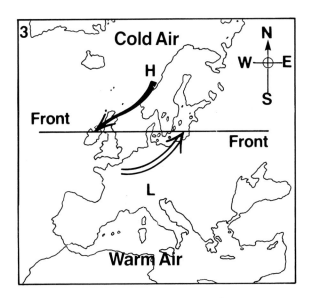

The air now begins to move around the high-pressure and low-pressure areas. The cold air blows south towards the western end of the front, ie west of the low-pressure area, and the warm air is pushed north against the cold air to the east of the high-pressure area.

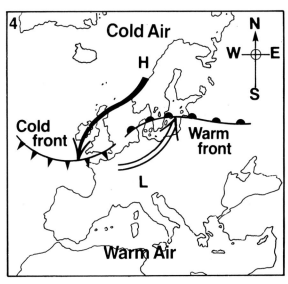

West of the low-pressure area the cold air pushes away the warm air, producing a cold front! The area which had the warm air becomes *colder* when the cold front goes past.

East of the low-pressure area the warm air drives back the cold air, forming a warm front! When the warm front passes it becomes *warmer* in the area which was previously cold.

FRONTS

We can distinguish between cold fronts and warm fronts. At a cold front the cold air pushes away the warm air. The cold air is heavier and forces its way into the warm air like a wedge. The warm air which is pushed away is forced high up above the wedge (above). On a weather map a cold front is drawn as a spiky blue line and it moves in the direction of the spikes. At a warm front the warm air moves forward and pushes the cold air in front of it. A warm front moves more slowly than a cold front because the cold air is heavier and more difficult to push. Much of the warm air also slides up over the cold. A warm front is drawn on weather maps as a red line with bumps and it moves in the direction of the bumps.

Clouds and Precipitation

WATER VAPOUR AND CLOUD DROPLETS

When water boils in a saucepan, water vapour is formed. This is hot gas which leaves the surface of the water. We say that the water is evaporating, that is it is being turned into a gas. It is this water vapour which tries to lift the lid of the saucepan and whistles when it comes through the spout of a whistling kettle (above). When the water vapour leaves the surface of the boiling water, it cools down and condenses, forming tiny drops of water. The hot water vapour is invisible but we can see all the tiny drops of water as 'steam' which hangs over the saucepan.

Clouds are formed in the same way. When water vapour rises in nature it cools down and begins to condense. The invisible vapour turns into billions of tiny droplets of water called cloud droplets.

A cloud droplet is so small that a pin-head looks like a huge ball in comparison (left). Since cloud droplets are so small and weigh almost nothing they float in the air.

cloud droplet

pin-head

35

HOW CLOUDS ARE FORMED

In Nature, air rises for several different reasons. So there are several different kinds of cloud.

Air also rises to great heights at fronts (above). Warm air is forced up by cold air and cools and condenses. Over large areas the warm air slides upwards along the wedged-shaped surface of the front, creating spread-out sheets of cloud in several layers. This type of cloud is called stratus.

If a small patch of air is heated up by the ground, an isolated cloud forms when it rises up in a column and condenses (above). This process is called convection and the cloud formed by it usually has a flat base with a rounded, irregular top. The cloud resembles a heap and is called cumulus. These clouds are very common, especially in summer. They are usually formed over land during the day when the air near the ground is heated up and rises. At the same time there may be no clouds over lakes or the sea because water does not heat up so quickly.

In the same way fields heat up more rapidly than forests. When cumulus clouds are formed at great heights they move with high-altitude winds which are usually not the same as those which blow near the ground.

When air blows against a mountain or a hill, it is forced to rise to get over the top. Thus it cools and condenses and a cloud forms on the side of the mountain against which the wind blows (above). On the other side of the mountain the air sinks down again and there are often no clouds or a few small clouds shaped like almonds or lenses.

MIST AND SEA MIST

Air does not necessarily have to rise for it to be cooled. It can also move from a warm area on the surface of the Earth to a colder area and be cooled from below, for example when warm, moist air from the sea blows in over land which is cooler. Clouds are then formed near the ground. We call this mist. Mist is, therefore, quite simply clouds on the ground.

On clear nights the surface of the ground and the air nearest the ground cool down more rapidly than the air higher up. The cold, heavy night air near the ground collects in hollows and valleys where it often forms banks of mist, especially where there is water or marshland which makes the air moist (right).

On cold winter days you can sometimes see 'steam' rising from the surface of expanses of water (above). This is warm air from the surface of the water which rises and condenses. This is called sea mist.

DIFFERENT TYPES OF CLOUD

Clouds may be formed in a variety of ways and because of this they have different appearances. They also form at different heights in the air. These two features mean that we can distinguish 10 different types of cloud.

Low-level clouds have their bases no higher than 2,000 metres (6,500 feet) above the ground. This is where you find stratus, stratocumulus, cumulus and cumulonimbus (storm clouds).

Medium-level clouds lie between 2,000 and 5,000 metres (6,500 and 16,500 feet). Such clouds are altocumulus, altostratus and nimbostratus (rain or snow clouds).

High-level clouds form higher than 5,000 metres (16,500 feet) in the air. These include cirrus (mares' tails), cirrostratus and cirrocumulus.

Stratus
This cloud looks like a uniform grey-white layer or like grey 'rags' which move quickly across the sky. Mist which rises off the ground often becomes stratus.

Stratocumulus
The body of these clouds are wavy with large grey rolls sometimes covering the whole sky. Stratocumulus is common during autumn and winter.

Cumulus
Cumulus are white rounded clouds with flat bases. They can look like little bits of cotton wool (which are known as fair weather clouds) or like giant cauliflowers.

Cumulonimbus (storm or thunder clouds)
These are formed when cumulus clouds grow to a great height. They look like huge mountains of cloud. They bring rain storms, snow storms, thunder or hail.

Altocumulus
These resemble large or small waves. Often they look like white waves with blue sky between them but sometimes they look like huge, heavy grey bags.

Altostratus
Altostratus forms a uniform grey-white layer over the whole sky. The Sun can be seen through the cloud and looks like a small white ball.

Nimbostratus (rain or snow clouds)
These are dark grey clouds which usually cover the whole sky and give continuous rain or snow (not brief, heavy rain or snow storms – that comes from cumulus clouds).

Cirrus (mares' tails)
Cirrus is thin, fine, white threads or feathers high in the sky. Sometimes the wisps of cloud are curved or in bunches.

Cirrostratus
This is like a pale, thin veil, sometimes covering only part of the sky, and sometimes covering the whole sky. The Sun can shine through it and there are shadows on the ground. There is sometimes a large white ring around the Sun called a halo.

Cirrocumulus

These look like small, white, fleecy waves very high up. They are a rather unusual type of cloud.

Watch out when you see these clouds – they mean rain is on the way!

Warning sign 1
Mares' tails (cirrus) with curved ends.

Warning sign 2
Cirrostratus with halo.

Warning sign 3
Altostratus.
Rain is not far off now.

THE 10 TYPES OF CLOUD

Cumulonimbus
(thunder cloud)

Cumulus

Stratus

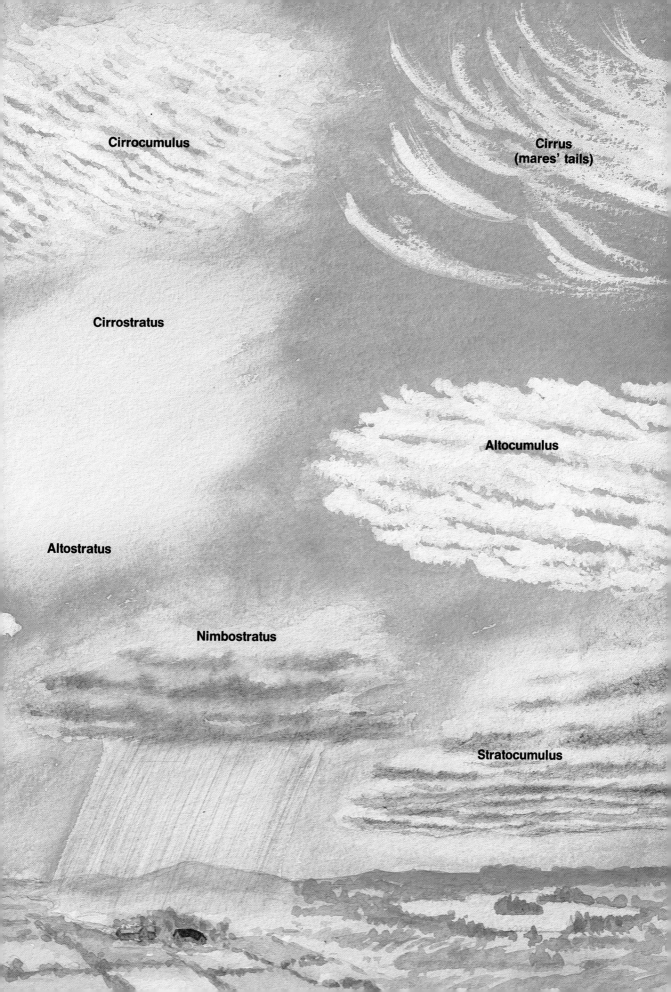

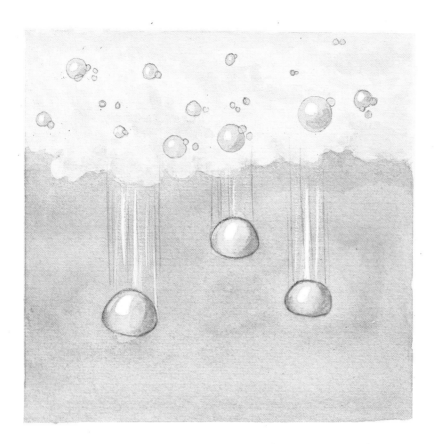

RAINDROPS

The tiny cloud droplets that form clouds are never still but are constantly moving in all directions. As a result they collide with each other and bump into other small particles which are in the air.

With each collision the droplets grow and become larger and heavier. Finally they cannot 'stay afloat' any longer even with the help of the currents of air inside the cloud, and they fall to the ground. It begins to rain (above). Each raindrop is made up of many thousands of cloud droplets.

If it is cold enough, small crystals of ice may be formed instead of cloud droplets when the air rises. A cloud may consist of cloud droplets, ice crystals or a mixture of the two. One part of a cloud may be made of cloud droplets and another part, perhaps higher up, may be made of ice crystals.

SNOW-FLAKES

If it is so cold that there are small ice crystals in a cloud, these will collide with each other and with other particles in the cloud and join together to form snow-flakes. When these are large enough and heavy enough, they fall to the ground. It is snowing!

Snow-flakes can look very different but they all have one thing in common. Apart from being very beautiful, they always have six sides or six arms (above and below). Catch a snow-flake on a dark sleeve and look at it quickly before it melts!

SUPER-COOLED RAIN, STORM AND THUNDER CLOUDS

When snow-flakes fall and become warmer, above freezing point, they melt and turn into raindrops. On the other hand, raindrops freeze and turn into snow-flakes when it gets colder. However, raindrops do not always turn into snow when the temperature is below freezing point. They may remain as rain in spite of being so cold. This is called super-cooled rain. But when these raindrops fall on a cold surface they freeze immediately. Roads and pavements can be turned into skating rinks in this way!

Storm and thunder clouds (cumulonimbus) are the largest clouds of all. They may reach from a few hundred metres (several hundred feet) above the ground to 5,000 to 6,000 metres (15,000 to 20,000 feet), and sometimes even higher. This means that the temperature is often above freezing point in the lower part of the cloud, which thus comprises droplets of water, but below freezing point higher up, where it is thus made up of crystals.

There is a lot going on inside a storm or thunder cloud. There are strong winds with up-currents and down-draughts. Because of this, pilots of aircraft avoid these clouds because they can be tossed about inside them. As a result, all the particles in the cloud, droplets of water, ice crystals, smoke and dust, are continually tossed up and down in the cloud, as if they were in a lift.

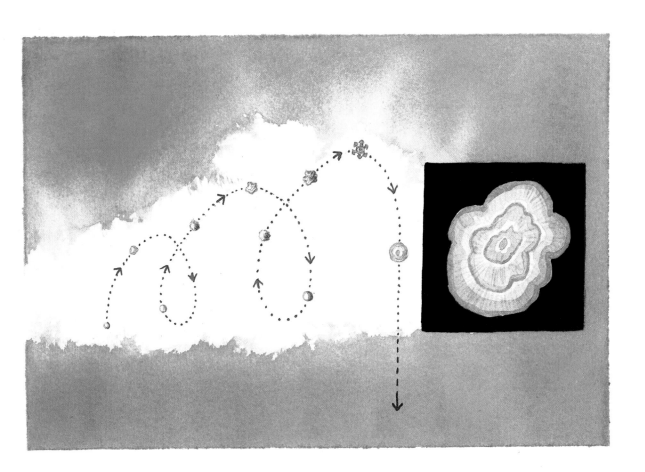

HAIL

Drops of water turn into ice when they go up to the cold parts of the cloud. When they fall down again their surface may begin to melt and other droplets of water may also collect on them. When they go up again the layer of water freezes. In this way balls of ice made up of several layers like the layers of an onion are formed (above). These are called hailstones. Eventually the hailstones become so large and heavy that they fall out of the cloud to the ground.

The field of corn on the left was devastated by enormous hailstones.

THUNDER AND LIGHTNING

Another interesting thing which takes place inside a storm cloud is the production of static electricity. The strong winds blowing all the particles in the cloud up and down produce positive and negative electrical charges. Usually the positive charges and the negative charges collect in different parts of the cloud. Positive and negative charges are attracted to each other, but charges that are the same repel each other (bottom right). Eventually the difference between an area with a negative charge and one with a positive charge, either in the cloud or on the ground, becomes so great that there is a discharge in the form of a huge spark (right). This spark is called lightning. Lightning restores the balance between positive and negative charges. It is much the same thing, although on a much larger scale, as the spark you sometimes feel if you stroke a cat hard or touch a piece of plastic that has been rubbed on your sleeve.

Lightning is hot and heats up the air around it to approximately 25,000°C (45,000°F). It gets so hot and the air expands so rapidly that, just as with an explosion, there is a bang, which is what we know as thunder.

You see a flash of lightning the same moment it strikes since light travels extremely quickly – 300,000 kilometres per second (186,000 miles per second). Sound travels much more slowly, at approximately one kilometre in three seconds (one mile in five seconds). If you count the seconds between the flash of lightning and the crash of thunder and divide it by three, the resulting figure is the distance in kilometres to the place the lightning struck (dividing the number of seconds by five gives the distance in miles).

46

THE WATER CYCLE

More than half the surface of the Earth is covered by sea. Water evaporates from the sea, lakes and rivers and rises into the air as invisible water vapour. You can see this process happening when a puddle dries up on a hot day. Water vapour is also given off by plants and trees. Winds can blow the water vapour a long way from where it started. Eventually the water vapour turns into clouds and rain, so that the sea, rivers and lakes get the water back again. Rain falling on the ground sinks into the soil and is either taken up by the roots of plants into the leaves and foliage, or runs into lakes and rivers and from there out to sea.

In this way water circulates between the surface of the Earth and the atmosphere in what is called the 'natural water cycle' (above).

MIRAGES

On warm summer days you may see what looks like water on the road in the distance. But when you reach that spot the water vanishes and you may see it further on again. This phenomenon is called a mirage. It is actually the sky that you are seeing, or to be more exact an image of the sky. The air nearest the ground, especially above an asphalt road, becomes so warm that rays of light from the sky are bent upwards when they pass from the cooler air above into the warm layer (above). This is why a traveller in the desert may see an oasis in the distance but never reach it.

Another kind of mirage is when you can see things which are actually over the horizon. Islands or ships can seem to float in the air on the horizon. This is caused by rays of light being bent so that for a while they run parallel to the curved surface of the Earth. These mirages are usually seen in spring or early summer when the cold sea creates a layer of cool air next to it.

RAINBOWS

Rainbows may be formed when it is raining and the Sun is shining at the same time. When the rays of light from the Sun meet the raindrops, the white light is split up into the seven colours of the spectrum and reflected back to the ground. In this way raindrops act just like a glass prism (far bottom right). You then see a rainbow with violet on the inside, indigo, blue, green, yellow, orange and red on the outside (far right).

A rainbow is always on the opposite side of the sky to the Sun. The lower the Sun is in the sky, the larger the rainbow.

Sometimes a fainter rainbow forms outside the main one with its colours in reversed order, red on the inside and violet on the outside (bottom). This means that the rays from the Sun are being reflected several times inside the raindrops before leaving.

Observing
and Forecasting The Weather

In order to be able to tell what the weather is *going* to be like, it is necessary to know what the weather *is* like now. This is discovered by different kinds of observation.

All over the world there are observation stations looked after by weather observers (right). Every three hours, day and night, observations are made.

Outside each station there is a cabinet called a Stevenson screen. This is painted white to protect it from the Sun and has louvres to let air into it. Inside the Stevenson screen there are various kinds of thermometer to measure the temperature, and a hydrometer which measures the moisture content or humidity of the air. Each station also has a rain gauge and a wind vane. Indoors there is a barometer for measuring air pressure.

At each observation the observer records the temperature, humidity and air pressure. The wind vane shows the direction of the wind. An instrument called an anemometer shows how strong the wind is blowing. The observer notes how far he or she can see towards the horizon, and of course what the weather is like: rain, snow, hail, thunder or sunshine. It is also important to note how much cloud there is in the sky, the type of cloud and its height. Cloud observation is difficult and needs much training.

At the observations in the mornings and evenings the amount of precipitation (rain or snow) which has fallen is measured and the highest and lowest temperatues since the last reading are recorded (there are special thermometers for this called maximum and minimum thermometers).

WEATHER OBSERVATIONS

The observer notes all the information in a book (above left) and later writes down the observation in a special code which uses only figures. This is done in the same way all over the world and is a sort of 'international language' so that another person can understand an observation no matter what language he or she speaks.

Observations from each station are telephoned to regional centres, such as airports (above right), which collect all the observations in their areas. These are in turn passed on to the national meteorological headquarters where a country's weather forecasting service is located.

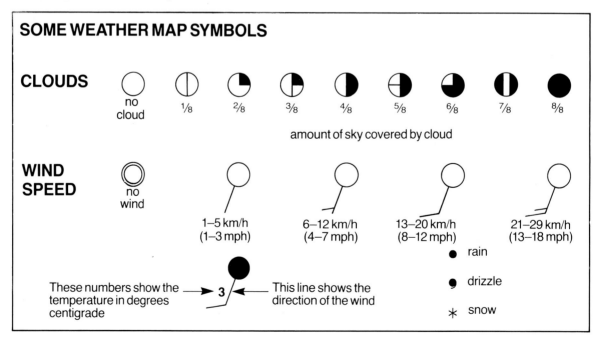

SOME WEATHER MAP SYMBOLS

CLOUDS

no cloud | ⅛ | ⅔ | ⅜ | ⁴⁄₈ | ⅝ | ⁶⁄₈ | ⅞ | ⁸⁄₈

amount of sky covered by cloud

WIND SPEED

no wind

1–5 km/h (1–3 mph)

6–12 km/h (4–7 mph)

13–20 km/h (8–12 mph)

21–29 km/h (13–18 mph)

● rain

🌧 drizzle

✳ snow

These numbers show the temperature in degrees centigrade → 3 ← This line shows the direction of the wind

The word meteorology comes from Greek. *Metéōra* means 'things on high' and *Lógos* means 'discourse', so meteorology literally means 'discoursing about (or studying) things on high'.

The national meteorological headquarters not only receive observations from the home country, but also from foreign meteorological services. In the same way the home country's weather observations are sent to forecasting centres abroad. Observations also come in from ships at sea and from automatic weather stations in places where people do not live, for example on mountains, or on small remote islands.

All these observations are written down on weather maps using numbers and symbols which are used all over the world (bottom left).

The meteorologist analyses the map by combining the information from all the weather stations to gain an over-all picture of the weather (bottom). This involves plotting and marking the positions of the various low-pressure areas, high-pressure areas and fronts, as well as areas of rain, snow, fog or clear sky. When the map is finished, the meteorologist knows what the weather is like, or rather what it *was* like since the observations were taken a couple of hours previously. This map is a synoptic chart.

WEATHER HIGH IN THE ATMOSPHERE

It is not just on the ground where it is necessary to know what the weather is like. What is happening higher up is almost as important. This information comes from observations from aircraft, photographs from satellites and from so-called radio-sonde balloons.

Weather satellites take photographs of the surface of the Earth so that forecasters can see the pattern of cloud over very large areas (below).

RADIO-SONDE BALLOONS

Large weather balloons are released regularly from some airfields. Hanging from these balloons are little boxes (above) containing instruments which measure the temperature, humidity and air pressure. The boxes also contain a radio transmitter which transmits the information to a receiving station on the ground. As the balloons rise, they are blown along by the wind and this gives information about the strength and direction of winds at different heights up to as much as 20 to 30 kilometres (12 to 20 miles) above the ground. Maps are then drawn and analysed for different levels above the ground – these are at approximately 3,000 metres (10,000 feet), 5,500 metres (18,000 feet), 9,000 metres (30,000 feet) and so on. These are called upper air synoptic charts. So now we know what the weather is like both on the ground and up in the air.

WEATHER FORECASTS

The next step is to discover what the weather will be like, that is to make a forecast. For this the meteorologist draws up forecast maps, both synoptic and upper air synoptic charts. Much use is made of computers, which are fed with all the information from observations and then, with knowledge about air movements, work out what conditions will be like in a few hours, the next day or a week ahead.

The meteorologist then has the difficult task of trying to tell if it is going to be warm or cold, sunny, raining, snowing or windy.

Most of the time the forecast is right, but now and then it is wrong. This might be because of incorrect observations or because there are not enough observations. For example the meteorologist may not have observations of what the weather is like out over the ocean. In this case the computers cannot work out what will happen either.

With long-range forecasts (forecasts of the weather more than a week away) there is a greater chance of being wrong.

Forecasts are made available in various ways. Radio, television and newspapers broadcast or publish weather information to the general public. Others who have requested special forecasts can get specific information by telephone or telex. At large airfields there are meteorologists who provide information especially for air traffic. In this way people can plan whether they should go to the seaside, wear their overcoats or whether they should take their umbrellas with them.

Ian McCaskill forecasts the weather on British television.

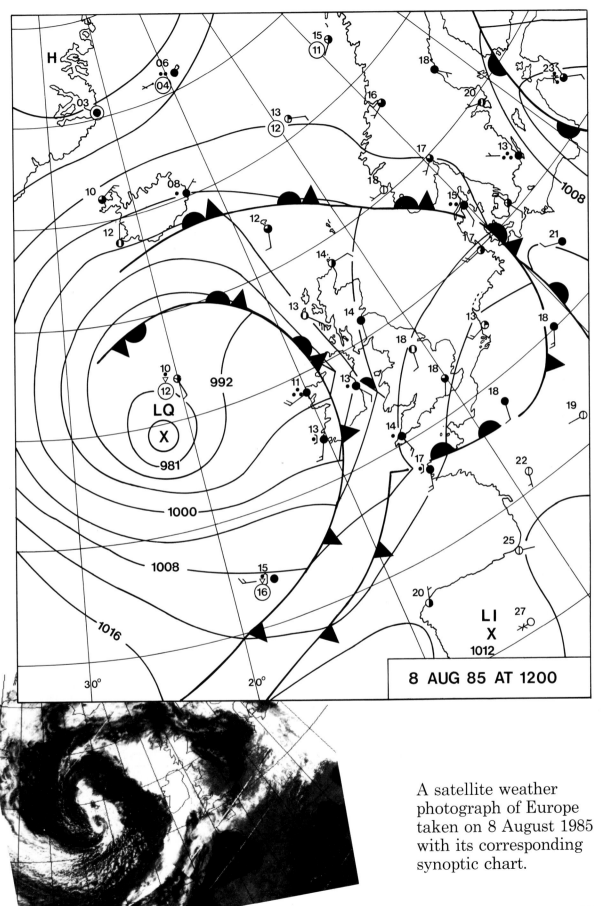

A satellite weather
photograph of Europe
taken on 8 August 1985
with its corresponding
synoptic chart.

TELEVISION WEATHER
MAP SYMBOLS

These are the symbols used in weather forecasts by the BBC in Britain. Television companies all over the world use similar symbols.

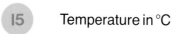 Temperature in °C

Freezing temperatures below 0°C

 Sunshine with temperatures in °C

Fine weather clouds that are thin and patchy

 Thick, widespread cloud typical of a dull day

Sunny intervals

 Rain

 Rain showers and sunny intervals

 Snow

 Sleet

 Thunderstorm

 Wind speed (in mph) and direction

FOG Indicated by words on map

Index